What's the Differe...

by Niki Davies

Section One:
Songs To Sing!

Series Editor: Sadie Cook
Text processed by Halstan & Co Ltd, Amersham, Bucks HP6 6HJ
Cover design by xheight design limited
Vocals on recording by Niki Davies
All recordings orchestrated and engineered by Dave Corbett
Published 1998

© International Music Publications Limited
Southend Road, Woodford Green, Essex IG8 8HN, England

Exclusive Distributors:

International Music Publications Limited

England: Southend Road
Woodford Green, Essex IG8 8HN

Germany: Marstallstr. 8
D-80539 München

Denmark: Danmusik
Vognmagergade 7
DK1120 Copenhagen K

Italy: Nuova Quartiere Industriale
Via Campania 12
20098 San Guiliano Milanese
Milano
Italy

Spain: Magallanes 25
28015 Madrid
Spain

France: 25 Rue d'Hauteville
75010 Paris
France

WARNER BROS. PUBLICATIONS U.S. INC.

USA: 15800 N.W. 48th Avenue
Miami, Florida 33014
USA

Australia: 3 Talavera Road
North Ryde
New South Wales 2113
Australia

Scandinavia: P.O. Box 533
Vendevagen 85 B
S-182 15 Danderyd
Sweden

INTRODUCTION

This book aims to provide simple musical material for pre-school children and Key Stage One pupils. The songs, actions, music & movement activities and performance ideas all combine to create a stimulating musical environment, which helps to cultivate and nurture enthusiasm for music in the very young. At the same time, the material is thoughtfully designed to gently stretch and improve the children's musical ability and build confidence in their use of language skills, body co-ordination, social development and awareness. The material is suitable for both non-specialist and music specialist teachers with the inclusion of backing tracks on the enclosed CD and easy piano arrangements in the book.

Section One: Songs To Sing!

The twelve songs which make up this section of the book all draw on the every day experiences of three to six year olds providing a steady learning process to help contribute to their development and knowledge. There are actions to accompany the songs, along with full versions and backing tracks on the enclosed CD. Through learning and singing these songs the children will experience an instant sense of achievement and pleasure.

Section Two: Musical Activities, Music & Movement and Curriculum Linked Activities

This section develops further the children's concentration and listening skills by exploring sounds through the use of musical instruments and by relating sounds to images and movement. There are opportunities and suggestions for the children to create their own musical instruments and to experience making music with these as a group.

The seven music & movement exercises use the excerpts on the enclosed CD as descriptive music for the children to act and mime to. As with other activities in the book you may only wish to use one or two of these excerpts, or prefer to dip into them over a term's work.

Section Three: A Musical Episode - The Magic Box Of Opposites

This short, easily producable musical combines some of the songs covered in section one with a simple script. The material is flexible enough to be adapted into an elaborate performance or to be kept as simple as you like. The children are able to develop more confidence in their musical and creative ability through taking part in role-play and performing their work to their mums and dads.

Whether used as an occasional resource or as a theme on which to base a term's work, the teaching ideas and activities in this book are designed to a clear, yet flexible pattern which is completely usable by musicians and non-musicians alike.

When You're Happy

Words and Music by
Niki Davies

7

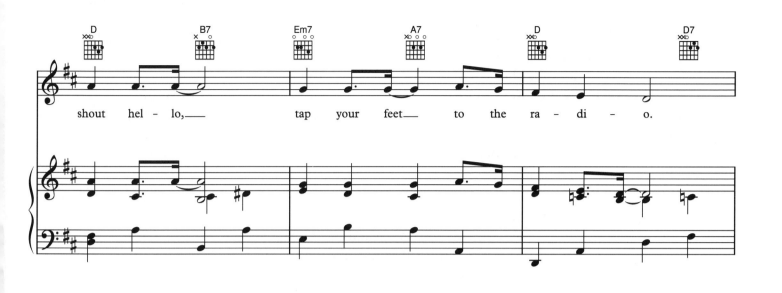

shout hel - lo,____ tap your feet____ to the ra - di - o.

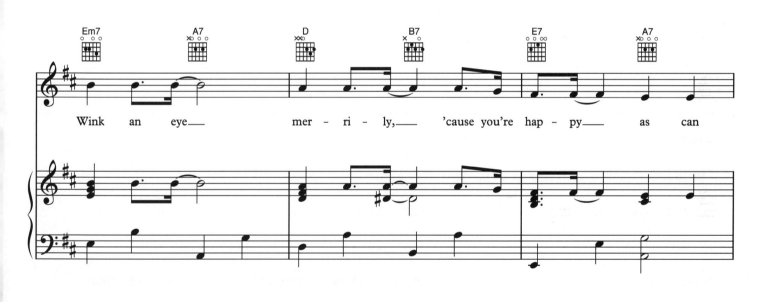

Wink an eye____ mer - ri - ly,____ 'cause you're hap - py____ as can

be,____ 'cause you're hap - py____ as can be.

1. When you're happy, when you're happy
   You can clap your hands and sing.
   When you're happy, when you're happy,
   You can do anything.
   So put on a smile, shout hello,
   Tap your feet to the radio.
   Wink an eye merrily,
   'Cause you're happy as can be.
   'Cause you're happy as can be.

2. When you're sad, when you're sad,
   Do you hold your head down low?
   When you're sad, when you're sad,
   Do your tears begin to show?
   You cannot smile or shout hello,
   Or tap your feet to the radio.
   You can't wink an eye merrily
   'Cause you're sad as can be.
   'Cause you're sad as can be.

BUT!
When you're happy, when you're happy
You can clap your hands and sing.
When you're happy, when you're happy,
You can do anything.
So put on a smile, shout hello,
Tap your feet to the radio.
Wink an eye merrily,
'Cause you're happy as can be.
'Cause you're happy as can be.

Actions

The actions for this song should come naturally - here's some ideas:

Clap your hands and sing   -   Clap hands with each word

Put on a smile   -   Make a smile shape with your index finger

Shout "Hello"   -   Place hands either side of mouth and pretend to shout

Tap your feet to the radio   -   Tap feet to the beat

Wink an eye   -   The children may not be able to do this but can have fun trying!

For the sad verse, repeat the above actions but in a sad, slow way.

What's The Difference?

Words and Music by
Niki Davies

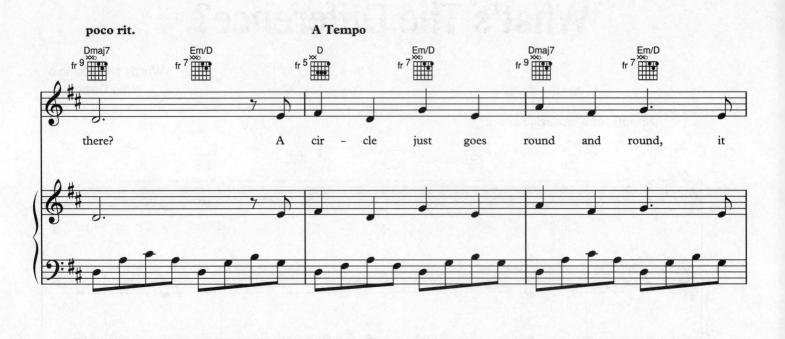

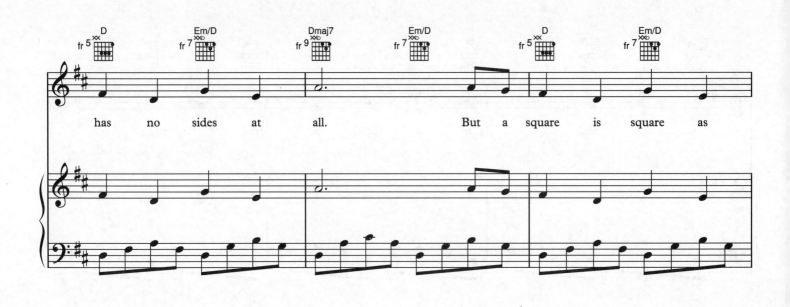

Draw a circle in the air
Now beside it draw a square
What's the difference, what's the difference,
What's the difference there?
A circle just goes round and round
It has no sides at all.
But a square is square as it can be,
With sides one, two, three, four.

Actions

The words suggest easy actions to this song.

A Rocket Is Fast

Words and Music by
Niki Davies

A rock-et is fast, whoosh! A

rock-et is fast, whoosh! I'm off to the moon, I'll

be there soon, a rock-et is fast, whoosh! A

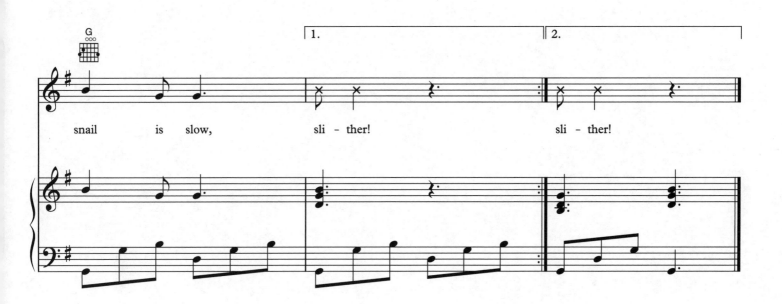

A rocket is fast, WHOOSH!
A rocket is fast, WHOOSH!
I'm off to the moon, I'll be there soon,
A rocket is fast, WHOOSH!

A snail is slow, slither.
A snail is slow, slither.
She carries her house wherever she goes,
A snail is slow, slither.

Alternative verses could be:

A leopard is fast, dashing along
A leopard is fast, dashing along
He dashes along, in a flash, he's gone,
A leopard is fast, dashing along.

A tractor is slow, chug, chug,
A tractor is slow, chug, chug.
It chugs on its way but it takes all day
A tractor is slow, chug, chug.

Actions

Whoosh!	-	Place hands in a prayer shape and 'whoosh' them upwards and over your head - like a rocket!
Snail	-	Put one hand out flat - this is the snail. Place your other hand on top in a fist shape - this is the shell. Move the 'snail' in a snail-like way.
Leopard	-	Make bounding movements with arms and hands.
Tractor	-	Pretend to be the tractor driver, steering at the wheel.

Money Spider

Words and Music by
Niki Davies

Will you bring me luck to - day? If I'm kind, please

poco rit.　　　　A Tempo

will you stay? Will you bring me luck to - day, mon - ey

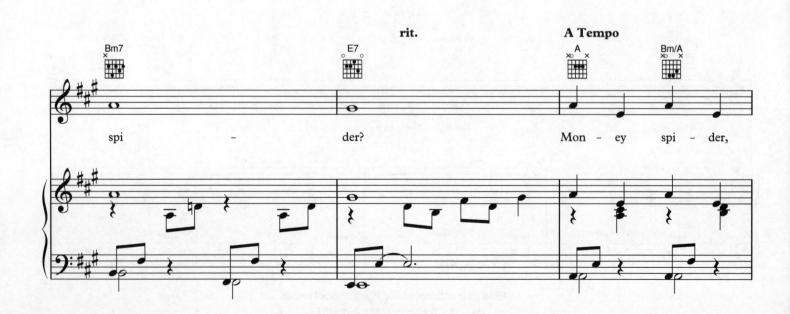

rit.　　　　A Tempo

spi - der? Mon - ey spi - der,

1. Money Spider, you're so small,
   I can hardly see you at all,
   Dangling on a tiny thread,
   Money Spider, Money Spider.

2. Just a little wriggly dot,
   Hardly big enough to spot,
   Dangling on a tiny thread,
   Money Spider, Money Spider.

3. Will you bring me luck today?
   If I'm kind, please will you stay?
   Will you bring me luck today,
   Money Spider?

4. Money Spider, you're so small,
   I can hardly see you at all,
   Dangling on a tiny thread,
   Money Spider, Money Spider, Money Spider.

Actions

You're so small	-	Put thumb and index finger close together - suggesting something very small.
Dangling on a tiny thread	-	Hold hands out together. Wriggle the right hand (the spider) down slowly on his thread.
Wriggly dot	-	Wiggle fingers.

Here Comes The Elephant

Words and Music by
Niki Davies

A heavy beat, but with humour

Hum - pha -lum - pha -lumph, here comes Jum - bo, swing-ing his trunk this

way and that.___ Hum - pha -lum - pha -lumph, here comes Jum - bo,

here comes the e - le - phant. - phant.

Here comes the elephant tall and wide.
He is gigantic from side to side.
Lumbering along with his great big stride
Here comes the elephant.
Oh, humphalumphalumph, here comes Jumbo
Swinging his trunk this way and that,
Humphalumphalumph, here comes Jumbo
Here comes the elephant.

Actions

Use your arms to suggest *'tall'*, *'wide'* and *'side to side'*.

Lumbering along	-	Use arms for big strides.
Swinging his trunk	-	Use arm as an extended 'nose'.

The Loud/Soft Band

Words and Music by
Niki Davies

hear you say, 'One, two, three, four'

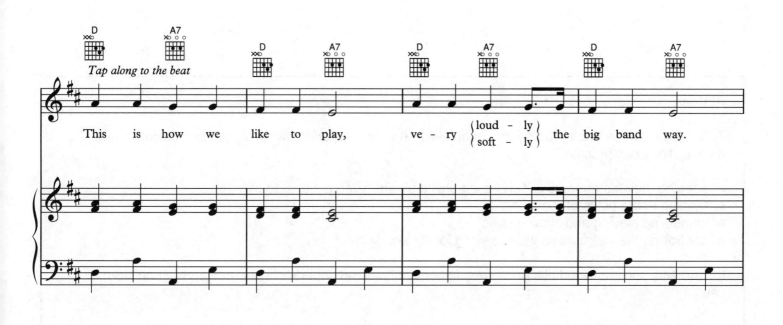

Tap along to the beat

This is how we like to play, ve – ry {loud – ly / soft – ly} the big band way.

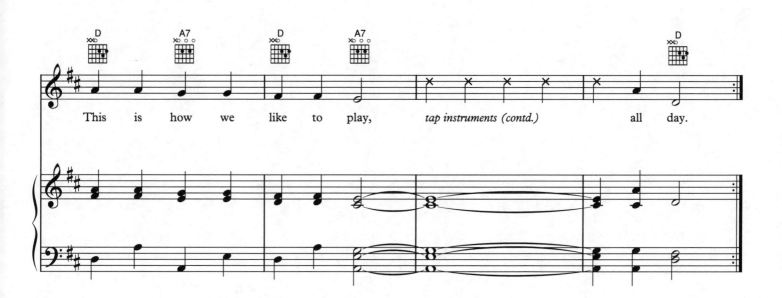

This is how we like to play, *tap instruments (contd.)* all day.

1. We're holding our instruments in our hands,
   We're holding our instruments still.
   We are a very famous band,
   And we will not play 'til we hear you say,
   "One, two, three, four"
   This is how we like to play,
   Very loudly the big band way.
   This is how we like to play
   All day.

2. We're holding our instruments in our hands,
   We're holding our instruments still.
   We are a very famous band,
   And we will not play 'til we hear you say,
   "One, two, three, four"
   This is how we like to play,
   Very softly the big band way.
   This is how we like to play
   All day.

Actions

This song provides good practise for young children in holding and playing simple percussion instruments. They can practise:

- keeping their instruments still and quiet until they are given a signal to play
- tapping to the pulse of the music
- combining playing and singing skills
- controlling the instruments when playing loudly and softly

Instruments such as wood blocks, claves, finger cymbals and jingle sticks are easy for the children to use.

Have You Seen The Motorway?

Words and Music by
Niki Davies

hun – dreds of cars go zoom – ing down, hun – dreds of cars go
one lit – tle trac-tor goes chug – ging down, one lit – tle trac-tor goes

zoom – ing down, hun – dreds of cars go zoom – ing down ev – ery sin – gle
chug – ging down, one lit – tle trac-tor goes chug – ging down ev – ery sin – gle

day.   day.

1. Have you seen the motorway?
    Have you seen the motorway?
    Have you seen the motorway?
    It's very, very wide.
    And hundreds of cars go zooming down,
    Hundreds of cars go zooming down,
    Hundreds of cars go zooming down
    Every single day.

2. Have you seen a country lane?
    Have you seen a country lane?
    Have you seen a country lane?
    It's very, very narrow
    And one little tractor goes chugging down,
    One little tractor goes chugging down,
    One little tractor goes chugging down
    Every single day.

Actions

Have you seen the motorway?	-	Hold hand above eyes and look from side to side
It's very, very wide	-	Spread arms out wide
Zooming	-	Zoom one hand across your body from one side to the other.
Have you seen a country lane?	-	Hold hand above eyes and look from side to side
It's very, very narrow	-	Hold hands close together
One little tractor etc	-	Pretend to be the tractor driver behind the wheel and 'chug' in time to the music

What Do I See Way Above?

Words and Music by
Niki Davies

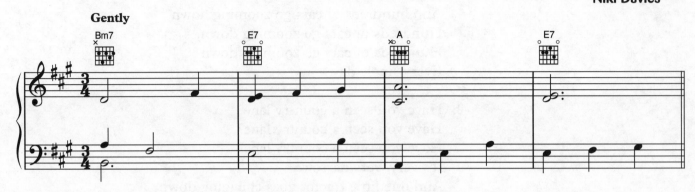

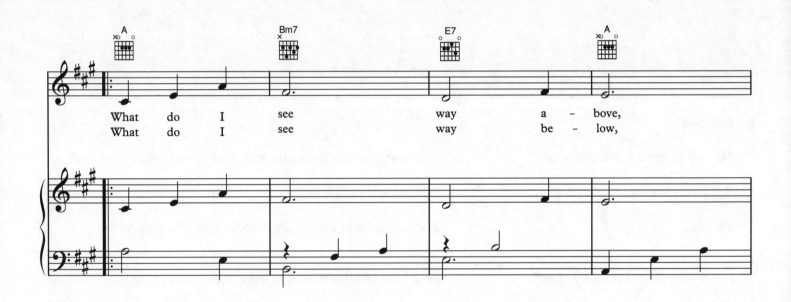

What do I see way a - bove,
What do I see way be - low,

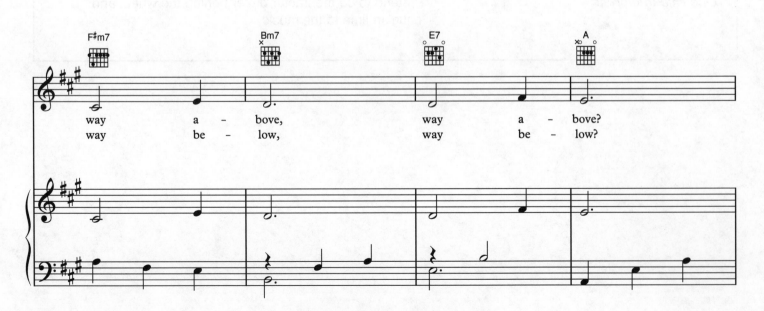

way a - bove, way a - bove?
way be - low, way be - low?

1. What do I see way above,
    Way above, way above?
    Sky of blue and soft white clouds,
    That's what I see way above.

2. What do I see way below,
    Way below, way below?
    Green, green grass and buttercups,
    That's what I see down below.

Ideas for more verses could be:

Above: White mountain tops and sun shining bright
or, Twinkling stars in a sky of black
or, A bright yellow moon looking at me

Below: The pavement grey beneath my feet
or, The sea of blue and a sandy beach

Actions

Look or point above and below throughout the song.

The children could also think up some other actions , e.g. for *soft white clouds, white mountain tops* or *sea of blue.*

Ten Clean, Shiny Children

Words and Music by
Niki Davies

Ten___ muck-y child – ren must get clean with-out de – lay.___ Now they can all get dir – ty a-gain; Hoo – ray, hoo-ray, hoo – ray!

1. Ten, clean, shiny children
   Have all gone out to play
   Two get very dirty
   And their mums take them away.

2. Eight, clean, shiny children
   Have all gone out to play
   Two get very dirty
   And their mums take them away.

3. Six, clean, shiny children
   Have all gone out to play
   Two get very dirty
   And their mums take them away.

4. Four, clean, shiny children
   Have all gone out to play
   Two get very dirty
   And their mums take them away.

5. Two, clean, shiny children
   Have both gone out to play
   Both get very dirty
   And their mums take them away.

6. Ten mucky children
   Must get clean without delay.
   Now they (we) can all get dirty again;
   Hooray, hooray, hooray!

Actions

The numbers 10, 8, 6, 4 and 2 can be displayed on you fingers; or you could act out the whole song with 10 children and 10 mums - gradually dropping out from singing as they get dirty.

Butterfly

**Words and Music by
Niki Davies**

1. Butterfly, butterfly, flitting by,
   Butterfly, butterfly, wings so bright,
   Now you're so close you could touch my face,
   Flutter by, flutter by butterfly.

2. Butterfly, butterfly, flitting by,
   Butterfly, butterfly, wings so bright,
   Fly on the breeze 'til you're far away,
   Flutter by, flutter by butterfly.

Actions

Link hands together with your thumbs and wiggle fingers to imitate a butterfly flying.

Jack In The Box

**Words and Music by
Niki Davies**

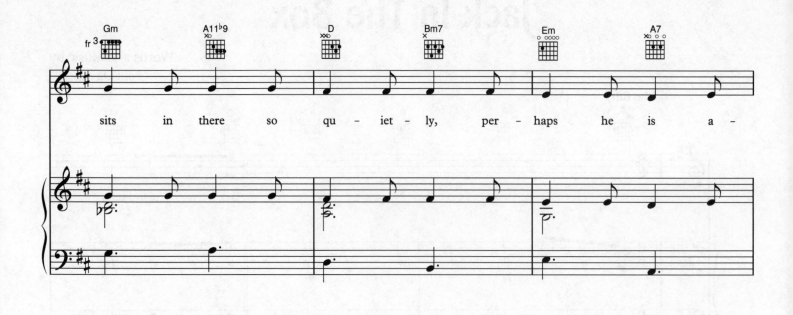

sits in there so qu – iet – ly, per – haps he is a –

–sleep, but just when you think he's gone to bed,_____

POP! Out he leaps!

Jack is inside, Jack is inside,
Jack is inside his box.
He hides away night and day
Jack is inside his box.
He sits in there so quietly,
Perhaps he is asleep,
But just when you think he's gone to bed,
POP! Out he leaps!

Actions

Jack is inside	-	Cross arms across body
So quietly	-	Place index finger in front of lips
Perhaps he is asleep	-	Rest head on hands
POP! Out he leaps!	-	Jump up with arms and legs out wide

It's An Opposites Day

Words and Music by
Niki Davies

1. Stand right up (Stand right up)
    Sit right down (Sit right down)
    Stretch up high (Stretch up high)
    Touch the ground (Touch the ground)
    Clap your hands, stamp your feet
    It's an opposites day today

2. Close your eyes (Close your eyes)
    Open them wide (Open them wide)
    Look to the left (Look to the left)
    Look to the right (Look to the right)
    Clap your hands, stamp your feet
    It's an opposites day today

3. Point to the front (Point to the front)
    Point behind (Point behind)
    Look very mean (Look very mean)
    Look very kind (Look very kind)
    Clap your hands, stamp your feet
    It's an opposites day today

4. Sing quite soft (Sing quite soft)
    Sing quite loud (Sing quite loud)
    Stand very still (Stand very still)
    Turn around (Turn around)
    Clap your hands, stamp your feet
    It's an opposites day today

Actions

As you can see, the actions are self explanatory in this song. As it is an echo song the children can copy the teacher.

Section Two:
Musical Activity - Sound effects to a short story

The Party

Five excited creatures came to a party,
A very slow snail,
A very fast leopard,
A tiny little wriggly spider,
A great big lumbering elephant,
And a quiet butterfly who fluttered closer and closer and closer.
They had a lovely time, all together.

Then they went home.
First the very slow snail,
Then the very fast leopard,
Then the tiny little wriggly spider,
Then the great big elephant,
And lastly, the butterfly, who fluttered further and further and further
away until you couldn't see him at all.

Experiment with tuned and untuned percussion instruments, and perhaps some home-made musical instruments, to find sounds which will portray all the animals in the story. The following sound descriptions will give you some ideas:

Snail Music	-	Slow, slimy sounds
Leopard Music	-	Bounding, running, fast sounds
Wriggly Spider Music	-	High, soft, wriggling patterns
Elephant Music	-	Loud, heavy, lumbering sounds
Butterfly Music	-	Floaty, soft, fluttering sounds

Give each child (or group of children) an instrument to play and make sure they know which animal that instrument represents. Get them to practise playing their instruments and to follow signals from you for which animals should play and which should remain silent. You could indicate this by pointing to each relevant group of children or by holding up pictures of the different animals as you want them to play. Also practise playing the instruments loudly and softly and gradually getting louder and then softer.

When the children are used to their animals and instruments you can begin to add the sound effects to the story as it is read. The animals should begin playing as they arrive at the party until all animals are playing together. They will then gradually stop playing as they all go home, leaving only the butterfly at the end. (This is a good time for the butterfly to demonstrate its ability to play softer and softer as it flies away.)

Further work with tuned & untuned percussion

The Opposites Orchestra

Gather together a variety of tuned and untuned percussion instruments along with any home-made instruments you can find and let all the children choose an instrument to play. Group the children who have chosen similar instruments together and get all the children to sit on the floor in front of you.

Explain that they are **The Opposites Orchestra** and that you are the conductor of the orchestra. Ask the children to identify various opposites in their orchestra, for example:

Instruments which:

make a <u>high</u> sound	-	make a <u>low</u> sound
make a <u>loud</u> sound	-	make a <u>quiet</u> sound
make a <u>smooth</u> sound	-	make a <u>rough</u> sound

They can also practise <u>playing</u> opposites, for example:

By playing:

very fast	-	very slow
very loud	-	very quiet
very smooth	-	very jagged

As the conductor of the band, create some hand signals which instruct **The Opposites Orchestra** to play in a certain way (ie loud, soft, fast, slow, high, low etc). The children should recognise these signals and play accordingly. You may wish to use word cards for the signals to aid reading and word recognition. Why not let the children have turns at being the conductor too?

Section Two:
Music & Movement

Use the backing tracks on the enclosed CD for the children to act and mime out the following (each track is one minute long):

1. **Money Spider**
   Tiny, fragile, wriggly

2. **Elephant**
   Enormous, strong, heavy

3. **Leopard**
   Fast, agile

4. **Snail**
   Slow, meandering

5. **Grasshoppers**
   Jumpy, jerky

6. **Swan**
   Smooth, graceful

7. **Jack in the Box**
   In/Out (some of the children could be Jack, crouched inside his box, whilst the others creep around Jack carefully and quietly, getting a big surprise when he finally leaps out of his box)

Curriculum Linked Activities

MATHS

Collect together a selection of different shaped objects and get the children to group these into opposites. For example: circles - squares; straight things - bent things; big objects - small objects etc.

ART/ENVIRONMENT

Draw or paint the following:

Something which makes a <u>loud</u> sound - something which makes a <u>soft</u> sound
Something which moves <u>fast</u> - something which moves <u>slowly</u>
<u>Inside</u> your house - <u>Outside</u> your house
What is in the sky <u>above</u> - What is on the ground <u>below</u>

You could also choose to expand on some of the links that the songs in section one make with the key stage one science curriculum, such as:

A Rocket Is Fast	Light and sound Forces and motion
Money Spider	Living things in their environment
What Do I See Way Above?	Light and sound

Section Three:
A Musical Episode - The Magic Box Of Opposites

Using all the songs learnt in section one, the children can now create a small performance to present to an audience. The theme of the musical is a 'box of opposites' which is full of 'opposites' words.

As the children pull out the various words, they sing a song about them. You can choose to keep the production simple by having a large box full of word cards which the children pull out in turn, or you may like to put on a more elaborate production. For this the children could all be inside the box in costumes which represent the different words/songs. They will jump up when it's time for their 'opposite' song and shout out their 'opposites' word.

Cast List

Narrator	The teacher or an older child would be ideal for this role
Happy	Dressed as a happy clown
Sad	Dressed as a sad clown
Fast	Dressed in a running/football kit
Slow	Dressed as an old grandad/granny with a walking stick
Clean	One particularly clean and shiny child
Dirty	One particularly muddy child
Close } **Far Away** }	Both children dressed as butterflies with large colourful wings attached to their arms and antennae on their heads
In/Out	Dressed as a Jack In The Box
Tiny	Choose a small child for this part - dressed as a spider
Enormous	Choose a larger child for this part - add a long elephant's trunk

For simpler productions the above costumes are not necessary. Each child can be given an 'opposites' card to take out of the box.

Scenery

A large, colourful box. This can be decorated with coloured tissue paper and card - perhaps using some of the 'opposites' shapes the children have discovered in section two (ie circles - squares etc). If you decide to put all of the children inside the box, try using lots of card sellotaped together at the edges to create a long piece of card. Stand this on it's edge and make a large square which the children can stand inside.

The Script

Narrator: Open the box, open it wide
What will we find deep inside?

Everyone: What will we find deep inside?

Happy: Happy

Sad: Sad

SONG 1 WHEN YOU'RE HAPPY

Narrator: Open the box, open it wide
What will we find deep inside?

Everyone: What will we find deep inside?

Fast: Fast

Slow: Slow

SONG 2 A ROCKET IS FAST

Narrator: Open the box, open it wide
What will we find deep inside?

Everyone: What will we find deep inside?

Clean: Clean

Dirty: Dirty

SONG 3 TEN CLEAN SHINY CHILDREN

Narrator: Open the box, open it wide
What will we find deep inside?

Everyone: What will we find deep inside?

Close: Close

Far Away: Far Away

SONG 4 BUTTERFLY

Narrator: Open the box, open it wide
What will we find deep inside?

Everyone: What will we find deep inside?

In/Out: In
Out

SONG 5 JACK IN THE BOX

Narrator:	Open the box, open it wide What will we find deep inside?
Everyone:	What will we find deep inside?
Tiny:	Tiny
SONG 6	MONEY SPIDER
Enormous:	Enormous
SONG 7	ELEPHANT
Narrator:	Close the box, lock it away And keep everything safe for another day.

[The children put all the cards back in the box and one remaining child closes and locks the box]

SONG 8   IT'S AN OPPOSITES DAY TODAY

You may want to choose a different combination of songs than those suggested above (maybe only two or three). Perhaps the children's favourites.

What's The Difference?
by Niki Davies
CD Track Listing

Section One: Songs To Sing (with vocals)
1. HAPPY - SAD: When You're Happy
2. CIRCLE - SQUARE: What's The Difference?
3. FAST - SLOW: A Rocket Is Fast
4. TINY: Money Spider
5. ENORMOUS: Here Comes The Elephant
6. LOUD - SOFT: The Loud/Soft Band
7. WIDE - NARROW: Have You Seen The Motorway?
8. ABOVE - BELOW: What Do I See Way Above?
9. CLEAN - DIRTY: Ten Clean, Shiny Children
10. CLOSE - FAR AWAY: Butterfly
11. IN - OUT: Jack In The Box
12. UP - DOWN; OPEN - CLOSED & LOTS MORE: It's An Opposites Day

Backing Tracks
13. HAPPY - SAD: When You're Happy
14. CIRCLE - SQUARE: What's The Difference?
15. FAST - SLOW: A Rocket Is Fast
16. TINY: Money Spider
17. ENORMOUS: Here Comes The Elephant
18. LOUD - SOFT: The Loud/Soft Band
19. WIDE - NARROW: Have You Seen The Motorway?
20. ABOVE - BELOW: What Do I See Way Above?
21. CLEAN - DIRTY: Ten Clean, Shiny Children
22. CLOSE - FAR AWAY: Butterfly
23. IN - OUT: Jack In The Box
24. UP - DOWN; OPEN - CLOSED & LOTS MORE: It's An Opposites Day

Section Two: Music & Movement
25. Money Spider
26. Elephant
27. Leopard
28. Snail
29. Grasshoppers
30. Swan
31. Jack in the box

Section Three: The Magic Box of Opposites
32. When You're Happy (Backing track)
33. A Rocket Is Fast (Backing track)
34. Ten Clean, Shiny Children (Backing track)
35. Butterfly (Backing track)
36. Jack In The Box (Backing track)
37. Money Spider (Backing track)
38. Elephant (Backing track)
39. It's An Opposites Day Today (Backing track)

In certain instances the arrangements on the recording may differ to those inside the book.

Reproduced and printed by
Halstan & Co. Ltd., Amersham, Bucks., England